The Gorgeous Girls' Colouring Book

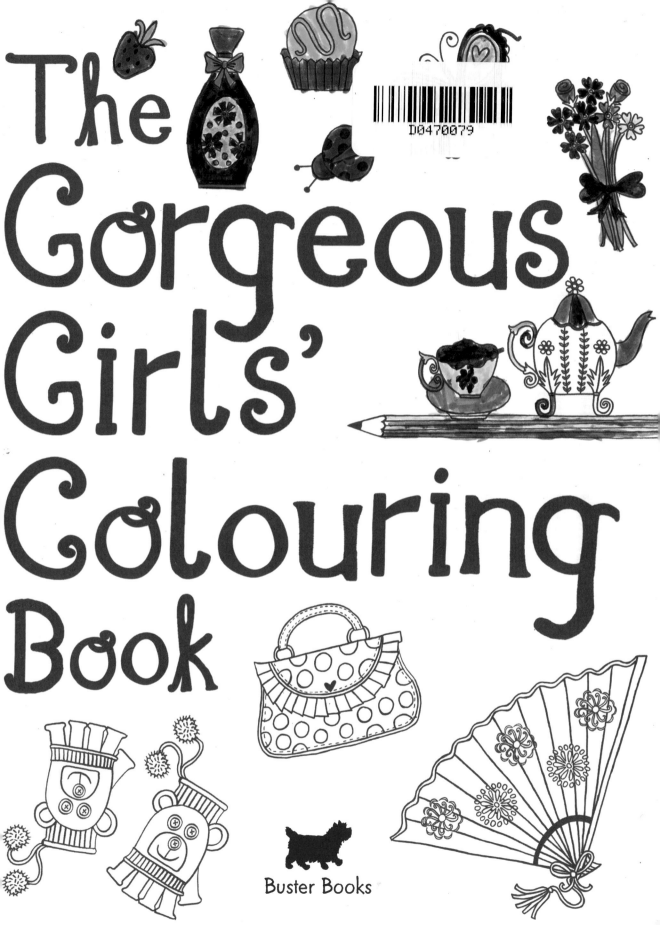

Buster Books

Illustrated by Jessie Eckel

Cover design by Angie Allison

First published in Great Britain in 2011 by Buster Books,
an imprint of Michael O'Mara Books Limited,
9 Lion Yard, Tremadoc Road, London SW4 7NQ

A CIP catalogue record for this book is available from the British Library.

ISBN: 978-1-907151-48-4

2 4 6 8 10 9 7 5 3 1

www.mombooks.com/busterbooks

This book was printed in February 2011 by L.E.G.O., Viale dell'Industria 2,
36100, Vicenza, Italy.

Papers used by Michael O'Mara Books are natural, recyclable products made
from wood grown in sustainable forests. The manufacturing processes conform
to the environmental regulations of the country of origin.

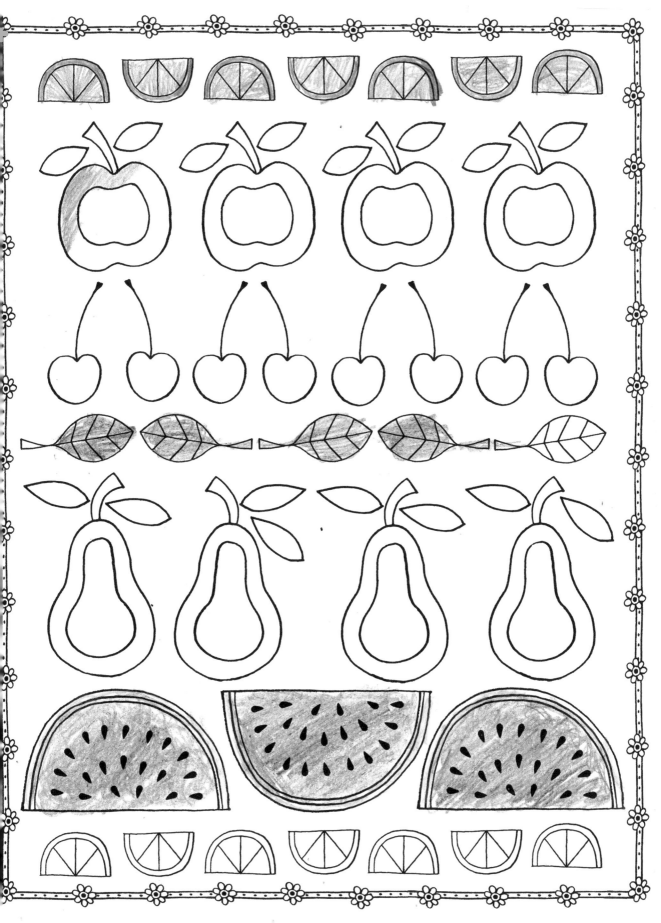

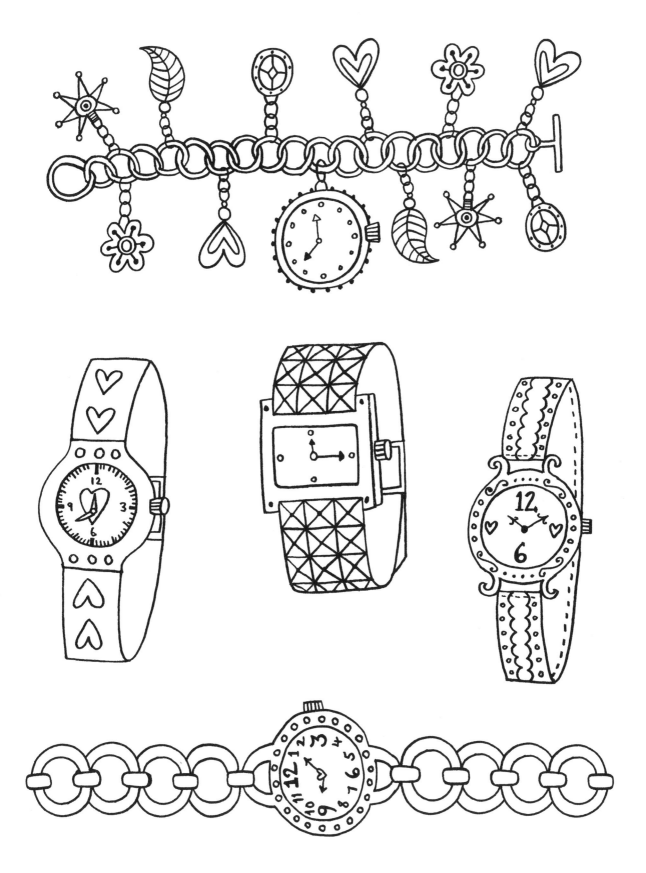

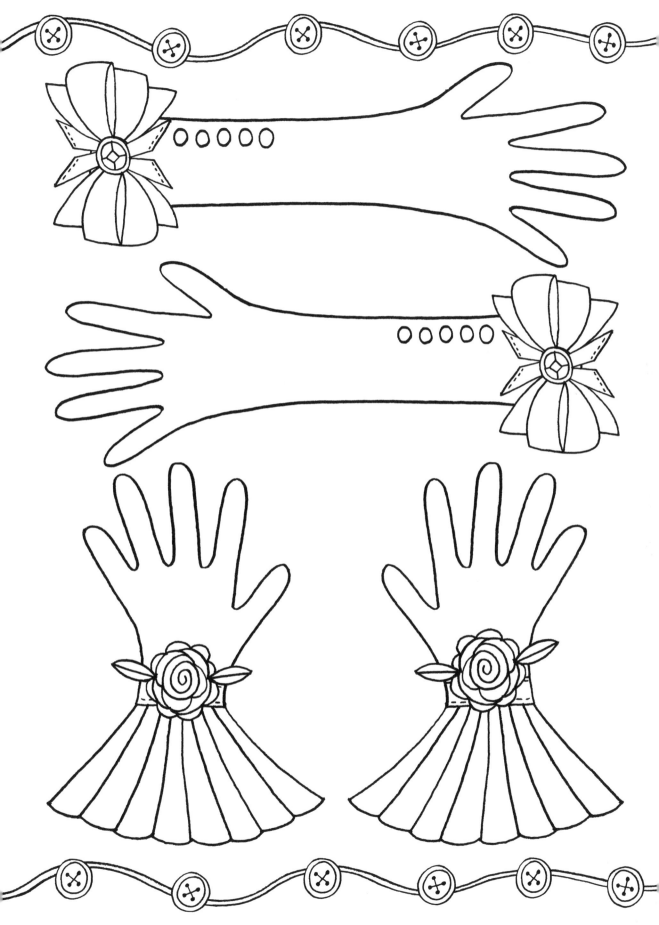

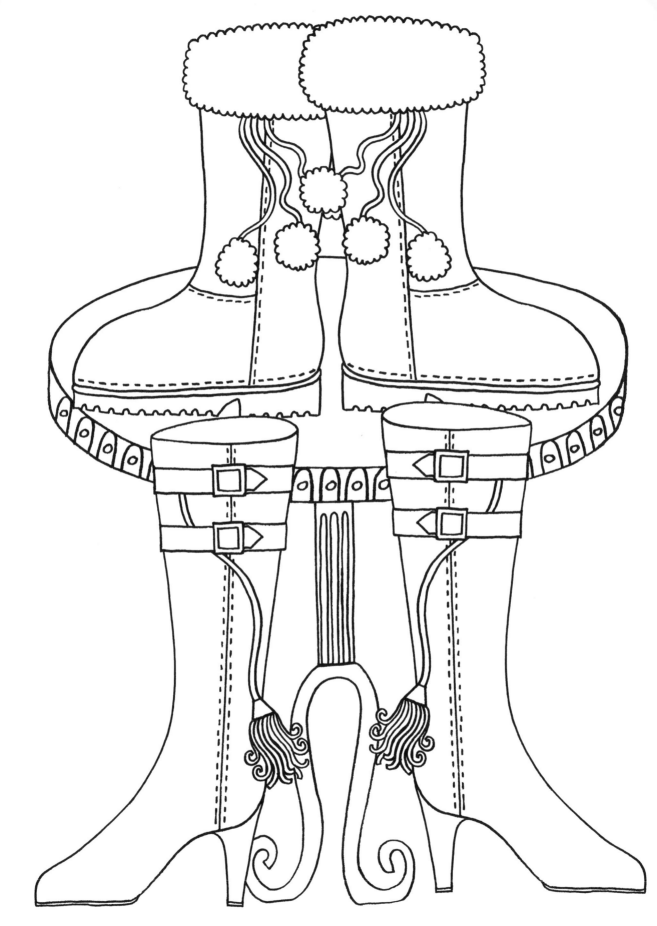

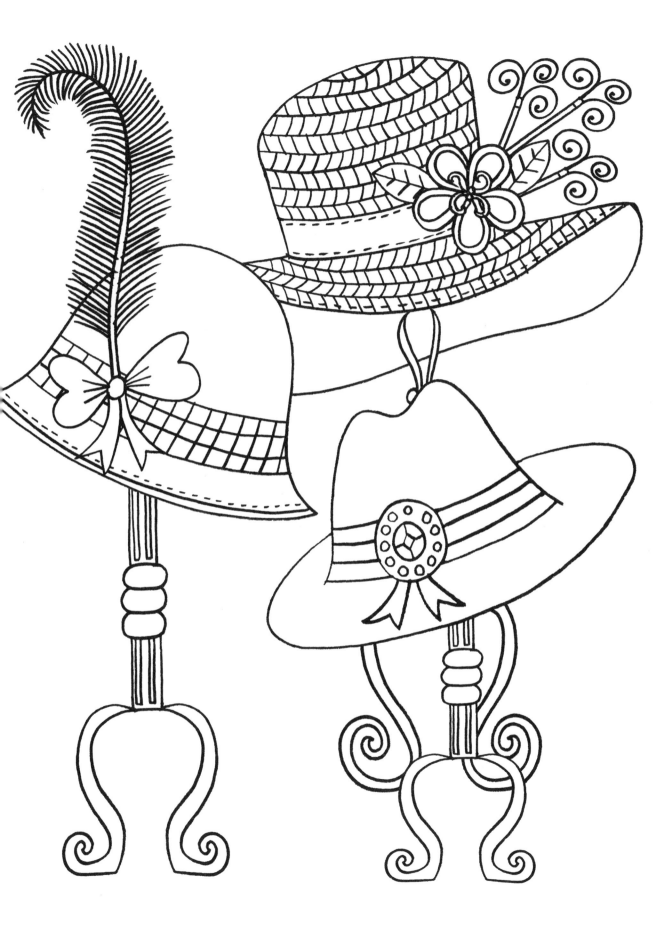